Picnic at
Black Rock

Picnic at Black Rock

Written by Leslie McGuire

Illustrated by Ron Lipking

HOOKED ON PHONICS™

Contents

Contents

Special Words

Special words help make this story fun.
Your child may need help reading them.

boat

fly

please

1. The Problem

This is Mom Bigg and Pop
Bigg and the six little Biggs.
The Biggs are not big. The
Biggs are little, but there
are lots and lots of Biggs.

Mom Bigg, Pop Bigg, and the six little Biggs want to go on a trip.

"I have a plan," says Pop Bigg. "Let's go to Black Rock for a picnic."

This is Big Bad Brad. He
is big. He is bad. He gets
what he wants. He will not
say "please," and he will not
say "thank you."

Brad thinks Black Rock
is his rock. Brad does not
like picnics.

Brad has a big flag on a stick. It says, "Black Rock is MY rock. You cannot sit on it. You cannot play on it. You cannot have picnics on it."

Big Bad Brad has a very
big problem, but he does not
know it yet. This will not be
a good day for him.

The problem is that the
Biggs are on the way to
Black Rock! Why is this
a problem? You will see.

The Biggs do not know
Big Bad Brad. But they will
get to know him very well.

But the little Biggs will have lots of fun! That is what they like to do, and they are very good at it.

2. The Plan

This is what the little Biggs think is fun. They like to play stickball and run up and down hills. They like to have snacks and swim.

They like to hop over logs
and zigzag in the grass.
They like to pick up sticks
and toss them. They like
to spin and skid and yell.

18

"Let's go on the bus," says little Gus Bigg.

"Let's take the bus to the boat," says little Ben Bigg.

"Can we please take the boat to the dock?" asks little Bess Bigg.

"Yes," says Pop Bigg. "The cabin is just over the hill."

"What a good plan!" says Mom Bigg.

But there are big problems with this plan.

The cabin is up at Black Rock, and the Biggs forget stuff...lots of stuff!

"I will pack the picnic basket," says Mom Bigg. "I want you kids to put what you want to play with in this backpack."

So little Bess Bigg puts
in a ribbon.

Little Gus Bigg puts in
his chopsticks.

Little Bill Bigg puts in
a bucket.

Little Ben Bigg puts in
his trumpet.

Little Bob Bigg puts in his plastic pickup truck, and little Brett Bigg puts in his puppet.

"We have what we need now!" say the little Biggs.

But they forget the ball and the blanket.

Mom Bigg puts the hot
dog buns in the picnic
basket. Too bad she forgets
to put in the hot dogs,
the muffins, the chicken
drumsticks, the eggs, the
ham, the napkins, and
the fizz pop.

Pop Bigg forgets to look in the picnic basket, but he looks in the backpack.

"This is odd stuff for a picnic," he says.

"No, it's not!" say the little Biggs. "We will need all of this stuff."

3. A Bug on the Bus

"Here comes the bus!" says
Pop Bigg. "Let's go!"
   The Biggs get on the bus,
but the bus goes six feet
and stops.

"What is it?" yells Pop Bigg. "Did we get stuck in traffic?" "What is it?" yells Mom Bigg. "Did we run out of gas?"

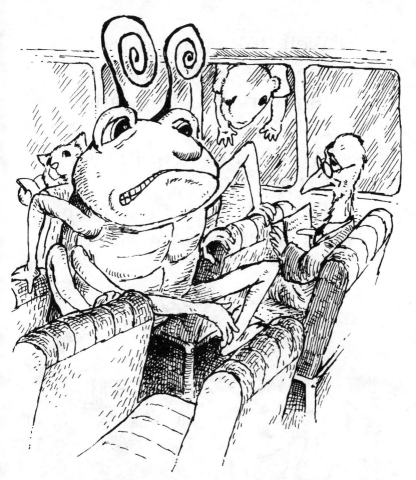

Gus Bigg takes a look.
"Uh-oh," he says. "There
is a bug in this bus."

"I do not think a bug in
a bus is a problem," says
Bess Bigg.

"Well, take a good look
at the bug," says Gus Bigg.
"It is a very BIG bug, and
it is stuck."

"We need to help it!" yells
Bill Bigg.

"I know!" says Bess Bigg.
"Let's get it with my ribbon!"

Bess Bigg says, "Come
here, Bug. I can help you."

Bess Bigg puts the ribbon
on the bug's neck. Then
Bess Bigg gets on the bug's
back. She helps him out of
the bus.

"Thank you," says the bug.
"Now that you have helped
me, can I please come with
you? I need a pal."

"We want to be pals with
you, too," says Mom Bigg. "But
we need to get in a boat. You
are too big to fit in this boat."

"That's no problem," says the
bug. "We do not need to fit in
a boat. I am big, so you can all
get on my back. We can fly
quick as a bug!"

"Very good!" says Pop Bigg.
"I am Pop Bigg and this is
Mom Bigg, and here are all
of the little Biggs."

"I am Bug," says the bug.
"Now I can be Bug Bigg!
Let's go!"

Up they go. It is a good
way to get to Black Rock.
They fly over the bus and
the boat. They fly over the
dock and the cabin.

"There is Black Rock!"
yells Gus Bigg.

4. What Will We Do?

When they get there, things look very good. They do not see Big Bad Brad yet. The sun is out, and the rock is good and flat, so the little Biggs all run down to swim. That is when Pop Bigg looks in the picnic basket.

"Where is the ham?" he asks. "Where are the hot dogs? I do not see the chicken drumsticks, the eggs, the napkins, and the fizz pop."

"Oh, no!" says Mom Bigg. "I think I forgot them all!"

"What will we do?" asks
Pop Bigg. "We cannot have
a picnic without all of
that stuff."

"I do not think we can,"
says Mom Bigg. "What will
we do?"

"I know," says Bug. "Pop
Bigg can get on my back.
We will fly back and get all
of the stuff you forgot."

"Good plan," says Mom.
"Get the blanket and the
ball, too!"

So Pop Bigg gets on Bug, and they fly off to get the picnic stuff.

"What do you want to do now?" asks Ben Bigg.

"Let's have fun!" says Brett Bigg. "We can play lots of games!"

They play catch
with slugs.

They play ball with cans.

They hop over logs.

They run to catch frogs.

They skid in the mud.

They fill Bill's bucket with mud, and then they drop the mud all over.

They toss grass.

They make a big mess!

That's when Big Bad Brad gets up from his nap under the cliff. He looks down. What he sees makes him very upset. There are baskets and kids and mud and buckets all over his rock!

"I am Big Bad Brad, and this is my rock!" he yells. "You cannot play here! Now pick up all of this stuff and go!"

But the little Biggs do not want to go. They get very upset, too. So does Mom Bigg.

"Is this your rock?" asks
Gus Bigg.

"Yes, it is," says Big Bad Brad.

"If we cannot play here, where
can we play?" asks Bess Bigg.

But Mom Bigg says, "We
need to go. This is Big Bad
Brad's rock, and we cannot
have a picnic here."

"You can have a picnic but not on Black Rock," says Big Bad Brad. "Now get all of this stuff down to the dock, and have the picnic there!"

They begin to pick up
the stuff, but there is a
lot to get.

Ben Bigg runs and grabs
his trumpet, and Gus Bigg
picks up his chopsticks.
Bill Bigg grabs his bucket,
and Bob Bigg gets his
plastic truck.

Bess Bigg forgets the
backpack, so Mom Bigg
says, "Let me help."

"Be quick!" says Big Bad
Brad. "I do not like stuff on
my rock."

Mom Bigg grabs the hot
dog buns, but she forgets
the picnic basket.

5. The Biggs Pick Up

"I will get the picnic basket
for you, Mom," says Bob Bigg.
Just then, he trips and
drops his truck.
Big Bad Brad steps on it
and zips down the hill. WAP!

Big Bad Brad's hat goes up as he goes down.

"His hat can fly!" yells Bess Bigg just as Big Bad Brad flops on the grass on his back.

Bess Bigg says, "I will
help you get up!" But she
slips in the mud, and she
lands on Big Bad Brad's legs.
KA-THUD!

Bill Bigg says, "I can help." But he drops the bucket on Big Bad Brad's hat! BLOP! The hat is now flat.

Ben grabs his trumpet.
The trumpet goes BLAT!

Mom Bigg runs to
help Brad.

"No!" says Brad. "Do
not help me!"

He gets up and puts
his hat back on, but it
looks very odd now.

"You are a mess," says Mom Bigg. "Let me mop off the mud."

"No!" begs Big Bad Brad. "I do not need help!"

That's when Pop Bigg and
Bug zip up over the hill with
the picnic stuff.

"What is this?" asks
Pop Bigg.

"Who is that?" asks Bug.

"He needs help," says
Mom Bigg.

"This is Big Bad Brad. He will not let us have a picnic on Black Rock," says Ben.

"I am Big Bad Brad," says Brad, "and this is my rock. No picnics!"

"We are so sorry," says Pop Bigg. "We did not know. We will go now."

The little Biggs are very sad, but they go to pick up all of the stuff.

That is when Big Bad Brad sees the ham, the hot dogs, the chicken drumsticks, the muffins, and the fizz pop.

"That looks so good!"
says Big Bad Brad. "I like
picnics, too."

All of a sudden, Big Bad
Brad begins to sob.

"I am so sad," sobs Big Bad
Brad. "I do not have pals."

"Oh my," says Mom Bigg.
"Why not come to this picnic?"

"Can I please?" asks Big
Bad Brad.

This is an odd thing for
him to say. As you know,
Big Bad Brad will not
say "please."

6. Big Brad Is Good

"Do we still have to pick up all of this stuff?" asks Bess.

"No," says Big Bad Brad.

"Will you let us have the picnic on Black Rock?" asks Ben.

"Yes. Please do," says Big Bad Brad.

"It will be good to have you at the picnic," says Pop Bigg.

"Thank you, thank you," says Big Bad Brad. This is an odd thing for him to say, too. As you know, Big Bad Brad will not say "thank you."

"You are welcome," say all of the little Biggs, the big Biggs, and Bug.

"I know I can be good. I
do not have to be bad now
that I have pals like you."

"Have a chicken drumstick,"
says Mom Bigg.

"Have a fizz pop," says
Pop Bigg.

"Thank you," says Big
Bad Brad.

"You can play ball with us,"
says Bill Bigg.

"Can I play with your hat?"
asks Bess Bigg.

"Do you want to play catch
with slugs?" asks Bob Bigg.

"Is this what you need to do
to have pals?" asks Big Brad.

"You bet!" say all of the
little Biggs.